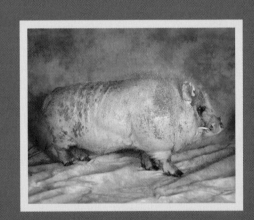

BEAUTIFUL PIGS

PORTRAITS

of

FINE

BREEDS

BEAUTIFUL PIGS

PORTRAITS

of

FINE

BREEDS

by ANDY CASE

photographed by ANDREW PERRIS

F

FRANCES LINCOLN LIMITED
PUBLISHERS

Frances Lincoln Limited
4 Torriano Mews
Torriano Avenue
London NW5 2RZ
www.franceslincoln.com

British Library Cataloguing in Publication Data
A catalogue record for this book is available from the British Library

This book was conceived, designed and produced by

Ivy Press
210 High Street, Lewes, East Sussex BN7 2NS, UK

Creative Director Peter Bridgewater
Publisher Jason Hook
Editorial Director Tom Kitch
Art Director Wayne Blades
Senior Editor Lorraine Turner
Designers Clare Harris, Kate Haynes, Caroline Marklew
Publishing Assistant Katie Ellis
Photographer Andrew Perris
Illustrator David Anstey

ISBN: 978-0-7112-3059-0
First Edition: 2009
Printed in China

9 8 7 6 5 4 3 2

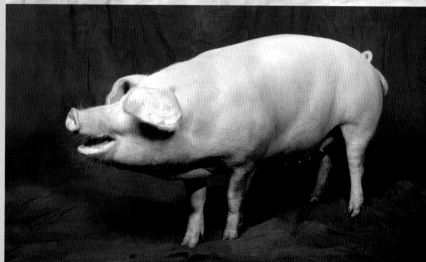

CONTENTS

FOREWORD

I HAVE BEEN INTERESTED IN TRADITIONAL BREED pigs ever since my wife gave me a TAMWORTH sow for Christmas over twenty years ago. She (the sow, not my wife) was grandly christened "The Empress of Cranborne" and ended her days in contented retirement after many years of productive motherhood.

As time went on, The Empress acquired companions. Thomasina, another TAMWORTH, graced the pig enclosures at Cranborne for many years. These two ladies were joined by other TAMWORTHS, some of them their own progeny, and by distinguished pigs from other breeds: MIDDLE WHITES and LARGE BLACKS.

The Cranborne pig enterprise thrived, and the pig population divided into two unequal parts. The first consisted of weaners, which we fattened and sold in our shop as sausages, pork, bacon or any part of the myriad things that you make from a pig. Many weaners ran in the woods, doing good to the ground, in a modern version of medieval pannage. The second and smaller part consisted of pigs bred for the show ring and cosseted in dedicated pig paddocks. We have had a measure of success showing the three breeds at shows and have even managed to win the occasional trophy.

Encouraged by the camaraderie of the pig exhibitors, we ventured to establish our own show at Hatfield and it is now one of the biggest pig shows in England.

The human race has not benefited from its increasing dependence on unhealthy food. Nutritionists, sociologists and politicians have begun to understand that the quality of what we eat has a profound influence on the stability of our society and the health of the nation. The traditional breeds are the guarantors of that quality. If they flourish, we will flourish.

That does not mean we should eat meat only from pure-bred traditional pigs. All of us value the vigour that comes from cross-breeding. However, we need also to ensure that the traditional breeds exist in sufficient quality and quantity to perform their role. How should we best do that? Paradoxically, by eating them. The more demand there is for their meat, the more breeders will respond and pig numbers will grow.

I would very much like to commend this book to you. You will see from the delightful illustrations that pigs are indeed beautiful animals. I hope this book will make all those who read it enthusiastic supporters of traditional breed pigs and even encourage some to take up breeding as well as eating them.

Lord Salisbury
January 2009

INTRODUCTION

"I like pigs. Dogs look up to us. Cats look down on us. Pigs treat us as equals."
WINSTON CHURCHILL (1874–1965), BRITISH PRIME MINISTER

HUMANS AND PIGS HAVE A STRONG AFFINITY. People smile when they see a pig – could it be that they recognise something within themselves that they share with the animal?

Like humans, pigs are intelligent creatures, yet their behaviour often appears paradoxical. On occasion, when the wind blows and it pours with rain, the sow will decide to turn her arc* around to face the elements. When the human goes to feed her next morning, the old sow is standing in the mud next to a mass of wet straw. Does this show stupidity, or had she tried and failed to do something clever?

Pigs may be stubborn, determined and single-minded but they also have a highly developed maternal instinct. Some sows are ferociously protective and will not allow anyone or anything anywhere near their piglets. Sometimes they bark a warning but often they run straight at you.

Piglets make great demands of their mothers. During the first 24 hours she will feed

Above: Sows have a strong maternal instinct and make very protective mothers; they are ever-watchful for the safety of their piglets.

them every 20 minutes, and every hour for several days afterwards. With some breeds, the sow will not get up to feed or drink for two or three days.

Despite thousands of years of domestication, the pig retains its survival instinct. It can eat almost anything with no ill effects. It is adaptable to different climates and weather and continues to live in family groups, if allowed. When a sow barks a warning, her piglets will immediately flatten themselves to the ground and freeze while the sow snorts and sniffs the air.

Pigs and piglets are very playful. A group of piglets will 'dare' each other to disturb a huge sleeping boar. He'll raise his head and they will run away, only to return and repeat the game. Some may even climb on top of him, but it has never been known for a boar to hurt a piglet. Time spent in the company of pigs can be therapeutic. As any pig owner will tell you, you will walk away at peace.

* See the Glossary on page 110 for an explanation of this and other breeder's terms.

PIGS IN CIVILIZATION

THE WILD BOAR (*Sus scrofa*) OF EUROPE AND ASIA was found in forests and broadleaf woodlands, where it adapted easily to the two extremes of climate. The heavy-shouldered body was covered in brownish grey bristles, which stood up along the top of its neck and shoulders, and it held its tail straight. Ancient humans hunted this wild creature for meat. Piglets were often caught in the chase and were brought home and tamed. Later, pigs were bred from and traded for pigs from afar, where the species had developed differently. These were then cross-bred with the home species. This first occurred in approximately 10,000–9,000 BC.

Pigs are not suited to a nomadic existence because they are not easily herded over long distances. The first settled farmers domesticated and bred pigs in the Near East in about 8,000 BC, and in China in around 7,000 BC; pigs were one of the first animals to be farmed. The domesticated pig spread east, south and west to Egypt and Greece. During this period, most of Western Europe was still covered in forests of

Above: Today's domesticated pigs are the descendants of the Wild Boar that thrived in the broadleaf woodlands of ancient Europe and Asia.

broadleaf trees, the perfect habitat for pigs. It was found that domesticated pigs thrived when confined at night and herded by day so that they could forage on acorns and beech mast.

Gradually the wild pig changed morphologically. Its head became smaller, its nose and legs became shorter, and its body longer and wider. The bristled hair became finer and smoother and the tail curled.

In the Neolithic period, the domesticated WILD BOAR of central and eastern Europe was interbred with pigs from south-eastern Europe to increase the size of the animals. During Roman times better breeding and feeding led to greatly improved specimens. The Romans cured bacon and made sausages but this knowledge was lost with the fall of the Roman Empire and was not rediscovered until the medieval period.

The pig was particularly important to the peasantry. Pork was the only meat available to the rural poor. Even after the First World War, it was common for rural workers to keep a pig at the bottom of their gardens.

DEVELOPMENT OF THE BREEDS

THE DIVERSIFICATION OF THE DOMESTIC PIG WAS, in part, determined by its local environment, which helped to develop the regional types. Until the middle of the 18th century there were, broadly, two types of domestic pigs in Great Britain: a small, dark, prick-eared pig that was mainly found in Scotland and a larger, lop-eared, white or bi-coloured one that lived in England and Wales. The different colours gradually arose as the colour of the WILD BOAR, and striping in their piglets, ceased to be so dominant. Small, almost wild pigs foraged on the hills and moorlands. The larger breeds of pig developed in different parts of Britain into different breeds: the EAST ANGLIAN, the BERKSHIRE and the WHITE YORKSHIRE. At this time NEAPOLITAN, CHINESE and SIAMESE pigs were imported, which dramatically changed the features of Britain's native pigs. They had 'dished' faces and were smaller and fatter. Native pigs were crossed with the imported species to give pig farmers the chance to breed pigs of colossal bulk (the 'spherical pig').

Above: An Oxford Sandy & Black sow with her piglets. One of the secrets of the pig's success is its ability to produce two litters per year.

Before Asian pigs were imported, Britain's native breeds had long, straight noses and long legs. New breeds evolved by means of husbandry and inbreeding. Traits considered undesirable in a pig were eradicated by eating the animals concerned, while specimens that conformed to the breeders' ideals were spared.

Pig breeding was not very scientific in the 18th century, and the regional types owed a lot to natural selection. It was a long process helped by the fact that pigs produce multiple offspring and are capable of having two litters per year.

The traditional breeds raised today have, in most cases, changed a great deal. They may be smaller or larger; their ears might now be pricked, when during the 19th century they were lopped. They have certainly changed colour. Tinkering with breed types did not necessarily improve vigour or the ability to survive. Natural selection became secondary to man's own criteria, such as docility, mothering ability, fertility, the ability to put on fat, and hardiness.

THE BREEDS

BRITISH PIGS ARE DIVIDED INTO THREE CATEGORIES: the Traditional, the Modern and the Commercial Hybrid. The BERKSHIRE of today is a Traditional, a black, prick-eared pig with white points, four white feet, and a blaze on its face and tip of its tail. In the 18th and 19th centuries it was ginger with black spots. There were other pigs that were ginger and black, such as the OXFORD SANDY & BLACK. When its society was founded in 1884 it was the most famous pork pig in the land and its fame spread all over the world. It had NEAPOLITAN and CHINESE blood, which gave it its dished face, early maturity and meatiness, and, early in its development, its production of fat, as was the fashion at the time. It was hugely popular, especially with the aristocracy, and even royalty.

In the north of England the white pig held sway, with breeds such as the CUMBERLAND, which was a coarse pig, not as big as the YORKSHIRE, but it had huge legs and flat sides; the MIDDLE WHITE, which was a small, white pig with a dished face and short legs; the LINCOLNSHIRE CURLY COAT and the YORKSHIRE.

Other breeds included the WELSH and, right down in the south-west corner of England, the BRITISH LOP.

The YORKSHIRE, which was later called the LARGE WHITE in England, is probably the most famous modern pig in the world. It has been crossed with every sort of pig imaginable around on the globe. The other modern breeds include the WELSH, the LANDRACE, the DUROC and the HAMPSHIRE.

Sadly, the CUMBERLAND and the LINCOLNSHIRE CURLY COAT are now extinct.

The most numerous of the Traditional breeds is the GLOUCESTERSHIRE OLD SPOT, a large, docile white pig with three or four distinctive black spots. The BRITISH SADDLEBACK is striking with its glossy black coat, divided by a white belly band just behind its shoulder. It originated on the south coast of England and has strong maternal instincts, rearing large litters. The ponderous LARGE BLACK glistens in the sunshine and has a mild temperament. But for a truly eye-catching pig, you can't beat the golden, long-nosed TAMWORTH.

Above: The Tamworth pig is named after the town of Tamworth in Staffordshire, England, and is one of the most attractive breeds.

BREEDS AROUND THE WORLD

THE DANISH LANDRACE HAS BEEN EXPORTED ALL over the world. The long, lean LANDRACE has very high fertility and good maternal instincts, and is one of the greatest reservoirs of genetic material for the pig world. It has achieved this status due to the exceptional diligence of the Danish breeders and testing stations where science has played a big role, keeping the LANDRACE pig quality very high since 1907.

The LARGE WHITE is the leading native breed in England and Northern Ireland. They are known for their large litters, their milking ability and for their strong maternal instincts. They're lean, active and sound. As a terminal sire they are supreme; the boar stamps quality and uniformity on all his sows, wherever they are found, all over the world.

The DUROC, a prolific red pig from the eastern United States, has been exported to nearly every country in the world as a terminal sire. It is the most popular pig in the United States and its influence is highly regarded. Its red colour was thought to make it hardier than black or white pigs.

The TAMWORTH has been exported to all the English-speaking countries of the world. It is particularly popular in New Zealand because of its potency. It is thrifty, hardy and very active.

The LARGE BLACK is a docile, prolific pig, and an exceptional milking mother. This breed is economically productive in poor situations and rough conditions. It has been exported to many countries, particularly Australia and South Africa.

The BRITISH SADDLEBACK is a hardy pig, a docile grazer and a good mother of large litters. It is used a great deal for bacon, when crossed with the LARGE WHITE it produces the famous blue-and-white piglets, which always fetch a high price at market. This pig thrives in hot climates.

Above: The British Saddleback is the pig farmer's favourite outdoor breed. It is hardy and docile and raises large, well-fed litters.

The famous BERKSHIRE has a smart appearance and was patronised by royalty and the British upper classes. This breed helped to increase pig production in Europe and the United States and has had an enormous influence on the world's pig industry for 150 years.

EARLY YEARS

THE SHOWING OF PIGS AT AGRICULTURAL SHOWS started during the 19th century, when most of the agricultural societies were founded. They also had classes for cattle, sheep and horses. In the old days, most stock were walked to the venue on the morning of the show or the day before. Pigs are not easy to herd any distance; they do not stay together because they do not possess the herding instinct of sheep or cattle. Pigs, therefore, were taken in some form of cart hauled by horses that were accustomed to pigs (most horses are frightened of them).

Before Christmas, fat-stock or prime-stock shows and sales were held, generally in the local livestock market, for porkers and bacon pigs, finished beef cattle, fat lambs and sheep for mutton. All the stock were judged by experts, usually butchers, and very high prices were paid for the prize winners. Butchers hung the winning carcasses in their shop windows with their rosettes attached, to advertise the good meat they had to sell. At these Christmas fairs or sales, the smaller farmer and the labourer also sold their snare-caught rabbits.

Above: At agricultural shows, pigs are judged by a panel of experts. Producing a prize winner is a source of pride and prestige.

They hung them by their back legs, threaded on a stout stick; bunches of holly were also sold.

The agricultural show is a shop window for the farmer or exhibitor and often helps to sell his breeding stock in the future, because if his porkers were successful in the show and the sale, buyers will come back for more. For the exhibitors it is part of the rural calendar and is very much a social affair. Families who may not have met since the previous year often attend a number of shows to try to beat each other with their prize sow or gilt. Despite the competitiveness, agricultural shows are convivial events and there is invariably a festive atmosphere among the exhibitors in the evenings.

Agricultural shows have always been important to rural folk, providing the best yardstick by which to measure their stock against that of fellow exhibitors in the ring. Novices can learn a great deal from keen observation of the 'old hands' and their pigs, and usually the successful breeders are only too pleased to help the beginner by passing on some of their experience.

SUMMER SHOWS

THERE CAN BE FEW MORE ENJOYABLE PASTIMES than showing your own pigs at a summer show. Some of us also derive a great deal of pleasure from judging pigs at the shows. I was greatly honoured to receive a letter from the Royal Agricultural Society of New Zealand asking me to judge the native Kune Kune pigs at their millennium Royal Show in Hamilton. Britain also has a royal show, plus the Royal Bath and West with the Royal Cornwall, the Royal Welsh in Wales and the Royal Highland in Scotland. Royal shows also take place in Australia, Canada, France and the United States, all during the summer season.

These days shows often have an educational slant. There are junior classes for handlers of pigs, sheep and cattle. There are stock judging competitions, 4H clubs for young farmers in America and farm clubs in other countries. Here the proper skills are learned, and often give novices a lifetime interest in producing proficient stock. These young people often go on to breed the prize-winning animals of the future.

Above: Summer shows are held internationally and are an important way for young farmers to learn the tricks of their trade.

Young pig breeders attain a wonderful sense of achievement when the judge walks over with the first prize rosette. There is an advantage for the pig breeder to go to an agricultural show: it could help him produce his or her own prize winner. The breeder can see other breeders' stock, and might decide to buy some in order to improve his or her own pigs. With skill, the new breeder can ascertain how a champion boar might overcome a fault in his sows, with his very good, straight walking action and his superior feet, the prerequisite for any show animal. It would be tragic to see an agricultural show disappear in any country; they bring the farming community together, not only by enabling them to show their best animals, but also by keeping the standard of stockmanship and welfare high. There is an exchange of ideas among the farmers and stock keepers that benefits all. Agricultural shows not only uphold rural tradition, they also express the character of the counties and countries in which they are held and celebrate the diversity of their livestock.

PREPARING FOR SHOWS

PREPARATION BEGINS A YEAR AHEAD OF THE SHOW season. Use your experience to mate your best sows with your best boar, so that the boar's bloodline and that of the sow will 'nick', as the pig breeder calls it. This means that these two pigs are so in tune with each other, they will always produce quality piglets. Matings must be timed so that piglets are born at two crucial times: January and July. Classes for young pigs are for the current January-born piglets and the previous July-born ones, and, of course, adult pigs.

Observation is the first task in selecting the best pigs to take to a show. Make your selection well in advance and worm them. Be critical. Do not take pigs that walk badly; it is the first thing the judge will notice. A pig's pasterns should be upright. It should walk with a straight action. Its front feet should not turn in or out. The back ones must not brush together. Any pig that dips in behind the shoulder or slopes off sharply at the hind quarter must be left at home. Furthermore, your pig must have a level back.

The second task is to train your pig to walk by your side, with the aid of a pig board (a square board that measures 60 cm x 60 cm (2 ft x 2 ft). You can also use a pig bat or stick. With a little practice you should be able to control it. A pig that is badly behaved in the ring won't win, particularly if it upsets the other pigs and exhibitors.

Finally, it is important to wash your pigs with shampoo or soap flakes. Make sure the inside of the ears are clean and that there are no lice eggs adhering to the hair of the pig. Rinse the pig and dry with a towel. Pure white pigs are heaped with wood flour (extra fine sawdust) to dry them and keep them white. It is brushed off before they go into the ring. Black pigs are sometimes only brushed and then heavily oiled with a paint brush dipped in oil. Some coloured pigs have oil lightly brushed into their coats. The TAMWORTH is never oiled.

In many countries – New Zealand, for example – the exhibitors put their pigs in the ring and leave the judge to move them on to see them walk. In other countries, they are judged in their pens.

Above: In preparation for a show, black pigs such as this Hampshire breed are often brushed and then oiled to enhance their appearance.

WHAT THE JUDGES LOOK FOR

GOOD JUDGE WILL WATCH THE PIGS AS THEY enter the ring. The judge will spot the pig that has something special, the one with presence. After closer inspection of this one pig, all the others will follow in order. In England, exhibitors wear clean, white coats and men must wear a tie. The pigs are guided around the ring in a clockwise direction. Any handler who walks a pig in the opposite direction is putting both handler and pig at a disadvantage. This is because the judge cannot flick his or her eyes back to compare your pig against the others, so will not be able to have a proper look at that pig. The judge must look to see if each pig has fulfilled the standards of perfection for the breed. The pig should have prick or lop ears, long or short legs or snout with generally 14 teats; and should be long or shorter in the length of its back, according to the published standard for the breed. The judge looks for a well-controlled pig that does not need to be chivvied along. A pig that runs from one end of the ring to the other is not being shown, it is out of control, and will be marked down accordingly. To stop a pig from running on, place your bat over its head and press back on its snout. Young January pigs are often very difficult to control, but do not run after them – they will keep running.

The judge will look for good or perfect conformation in the pigs. Most judges start from the feet up, so if a pig cannot walk it won't stand a chance. In a ring of high-quality pigs the decision is based on the judge's preference, with the one that first caught his or her eye usually being the first choice. Sometimes this might be controversial, but it was how the judge saw that pig on that day. The judge may receive comments from other exhibitors, mostly good humoured, if it is thought the decision was wrong, but that's the nature of the event. At the next meeting it could be quite different, with the second- or third-placed pig becoming champion. Showing would be pretty boring if every judge placed the same pigs in the same positions every time. It gives a breeder enormous satisfaction to win a large class with a home-bred pig.

Above: Judges look for a well-behaved, well-controlled and beautifully presented pig – but decisions can sometimes be controversial.

KEEPING PIGS

PIGS ARE SENSITIVE CREATURES. THEY NEED THE freedom to express their natural behaviour, to have daylight, warmth and bedding. They require adequate space, food and water. Pigs kept outside need to employ their natural instincts. What is worse: to keep a pig on concrete so that it cannot root, or to have a pig outside with a ring in its nose to stop it rooting in the earth? Pigs are gregarious and need the company of their own kind. They enjoy the sound of a caring human voice and the stroke of a hand on their backs. And for you, the joy of holding a newborn piglet is indescribable.

If you are keeping breeding stock as opposed to fattening pigs, it is best for them to run outside on grass. A couple of pigs can be kept in quite a small area, provided it is divided into two, giving you a summer paddock and a winter one. You can reseed them in turn. It is not necessary to spend vast sums of money to keep pigs outside. Three sheets of 1.8 m (6 ft) corrugated, galvanised iron nailed to four posts hammered into the ground, with four 2.4 m (8 ft) sheets for the roof makes a perfectly good house. In summer, put straw bales on the roof to keep it cool; the same layer of bales will keep your pigs warm in winter. During adverse conditions, nail a piece of old carpet over the front. Pig arcs or huts with floors are bad news; they harbour lice and rats underneath them because they provide a warm, dry environment.

When buying weaners for finishing, have them at eight weeks of age to take on to pork or bacon. If you want pork, do not keep them too long. Six months old is the limit, otherwise they will be too fat. When buying Traditional stock for your outdoor system, be sure to buy pigs that have been reared and kept outside, to ensure they are hardy and healthy. Ask if they have been wormed, and worm them immediately if they haven't. A weaner full of worms will not 'grow away'. It will carry little flesh on its back, and will have a bloated belly and a dull, spiky coat. Do not buy weaners from a market on a draughty day.

Above: Keeping pigs can be very rewarding. They are gregarious creatures and enjoy human contact as well as the company of their own kind.

CARING FOR PIGS

PIG PADDOCKS ARE BEST MADE OF 'STOCK FENCE', with the posts put in the ground 1.8 m (6 ft) apart and the wire fence strained up very tightly. Breeding and boar pens must be protected with a single strand of electric fence, because boars and big sows can push the unprotected fence over. Pigs in their natural state eat little and often, so provide their supplementary food twice a day, morning and afternoon, and stick to the same times every day. If you can get hold of fodder beet for the winter, give it to your pigs. It is high in energy, so it takes the place of energy-rich summer grass. The roots are sweet; pigs love them, because all pigs have a sweet tooth.

The weaning of pigs should be kept simple. Wean them at eight weeks old; by then the sow's milk will be tailing off and the piglets will be eating a considerable amount of dry food. If a sow with her first litter is becoming very thin, or 'milking off her back', be sure to wean her litter early, at five or six weeks. Give her three weeks' rest before putting her to the boar.

It is important to know how much space is required to accommodate the various sizes of pigs. Too few in a sty is a waste of space in the winter, because when it's cold they will lie very close together for warmth. A full sty will be warmer for them because they generate a considerable amount of heat. They will also make better use of their food and fatten more quickly, rather than using half of their energy just to keep warm.

Moving pigs from one place to another takes practice. Remember, all pigs have minds of their own. You have to make them stay together. There's always one that will try to push past you. Preparation before moving young piglets is essential: all small gaps should be blocked, because if a pig can put his snout through one, he'll push until he can get all the way through. Have all doors and gates open ready for them, shut those where they might escape. Keep the piglets up with the sow to move them along at a steady pace and use a pig board to guide them. Let them know who's boss and in the end they will be compliant.

Above: Allow your pigs to lie close together for warmth in cold weather, and plug any gaps that a pig can put its snout through, to prevent escape.

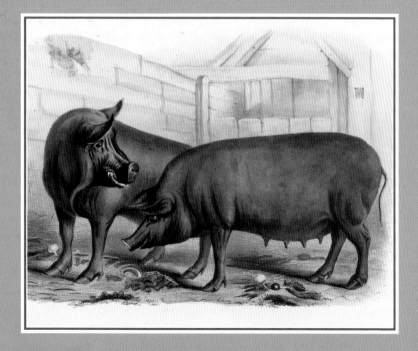

HISTORIC BREEDS

THE BREEDS in this chapter are truly the *granddaddies of them all.* Their INFLUENCE on subsequent generations of pigs can justifiably be described as 'SEMINAL'. Never before was *so much* owed by so many to so few. Behold the ancestors of our modern pigs *in all their original glory!*

NEAPOLITAN

The NEAPOLITAN pig from Italy was nearly always completely black. In the 15th century it was considered to be Italy's best pig and was used to produce air-cured Parma ham. It had a very fine, almost hairless skin that was wrinkled around its face. Like many other pigs of the time, it had a pair of wattles (jowls) under its jaw.

Features

The Neapolitan was a medium-sized pig with strong legs, a shortish head and short legs. It was long in the body with quite good hams and a straight back. Its face was slightly dished and it had ears that pointed forward. It was said to produce ham with the most wonderful flavour.

Size

Boar weight ....123–138 kg (272–308 lb)

Sow weight ....114–129 kg (252–285 lb)

Use

In Italy it was principally used for the manufacture of Parma ham. It was ideally suited for this as it matured quickly to give a lean, meaty pig. It was also exported and used on British and many European unimproved pigs.

Related Breeds

It has been widely supposed that the Neapolitan pig had Asian blood in its veins, probably Indian, which was crossed with European types. It is said that the Neapolitan can be traced back to the pig of Roman times.

Origin and Distribution

The Neapolitan was originally from Italy and the northern Mediterranean countries.

Italy

OLD BERKSHIRE

The OLD BERKSHIRE of the 18th century looked nothing like the Berkshire of today. It was not of uniform type: some were long and some short, and its colour varied from red or sandy with black patches to black and white. It had lop ears and short legs. By the 19th century it had prick ears and was heavier boned, but the colour still varied a great deal.

Features

During the 19th century the Old Berkshire was 'improved' by many breeders. Under Lord Barrington's breeding with Asian blood it became smaller and longer with fine bones and a propensity to put on a greater amount of fat. More improvement with Neapolitan blood gave it a finer coat and made it quicker to mature. Later the 'white points' of the modern pig started to be fixed so that it had four white socks and a white tail tip.

Size

Boar weight ....123–138 kg (272–308 lb)

Sow weight ....114–129 kg (252–285 lb)

Use

The Old Berkshire was a very popular pig. With Siamese and Chinese improvements it became lean and meaty, but because it was popular it became fashionable, and the excessively fat Berkshire was kept and prized for its size.

Related Breeds

The Neapolitan pig, which was mainly black with good hams and fine skin, was bred with the Old Berkshire. The Chinese pig provided fast maturity and fertility, while the Siamese made it smaller with better quality meat.

Origin and Distribution

The Old Berkshire was found in the East Midlands of England and spread to many other counties, except in the West Country.

East Midlands, England

OLD ENGLISH

The OLD ENGLISH pig was common all over England in the 18th and 19th centuries, especially in woodland. It was a large, hairy animal, narrow and short in the body with thick legs. It dipped in behind the shoulders and had a slight hollow in its back. It had a long narrow head with ears that hung down, and its nose was long, which helped it forage for food.

Features

The Old English appeared in many colour combinations, depending on which part of the country it came from: red and black or all black; red and dirty yellow with spots and patches of black or red; some were even belted with a white band. It had no jowl under its long head, and its ears were often held forward. It had narrow, pointed shoulders and chest with a crest along its back.

Size

Boar weight ....123–138 kg (272–308 lb)

Sow weight ....114–129 kg (252–285 lb)

Use

Many ran semi-wild in broadleaf woodlands. Some were taken in by medieval peasants and housed next to their cottages. This big, coarse pig was slow to grow and survived on scraps and waste, but eventually gained sufficient weight to be slaughtered for fat bacon and lard. It did produce some meat on its hams but this was usually made into sausages.

Related Breeds

The Wild Boar was the basis of the Old English pig. The Old English was also related to the very large farmyard pigs found in Warwickshire that were used for bacon, and to other coloured pigs from Shropshire and Cheshire.

Origin and Distribution

The Old English was indigenous to England and widely distributed throughout the counties.

England

SIAMESE

These pigs came to Britain in the 18th century. They were black or black with white; some were slate-coloured like the Neapolitan, to which it could have been related. The SIAMESE had a pleasing nature and an early maturity trait, which it readily passed on. It was able to tolerate extremes of hot and cold weather.

Features

The Siamese may originally have come from Vietnam. It was a docile, medium-sized pig with a belly that touched the ground. It had a barrel-shaped body, quite long with meaty shoulders, and well developed, rounded hams. Its legs were fine-boned and short and its ears were small and pricked on a medium-sized head with a straight nose.

Size

Boar weight ....123–138 kg (272–308 lb)

Sow weight ....114–129 kg (252–285 lb)

Use

This quiet, ponderous pig with its fine skin and thin, soft hair was principally used for pork. Its flesh was tender, white and of delicious flavour. In the 18th century the Siamese made a great improvement to the Old English and Celtic pigs of Britain, making them more prolific, smaller, finer-boned and quicker to mature.

Related Breeds

The Siamese was closely related to the Chinese pig and to those of Vietnam.

Origin and Distribution

The Siamese came from South-east Asia, particularly Thailand and Vietnam. It was used widely in Europe to cross with indigenous breeds.

Thailand and Vietnam

WILD BOAR

The Eurasian WILD BOAR (*Sus scrofa*) is the progenitor of all the pigs of Europe. He is of medium size with a long, almost prehensile nose and a narrow head with small upright ears. The WILD BOAR has bristled hair that can be very dense in colder, northern regions. From western Europe across to Asia they become smaller and are of different colours. The basic grizzled colour is a greyish brown.

Features

The boar is much bigger than the sow; he has enormous shoulders, which are protected by large shields of thick, solid gristle. His neck runs into a hump on top of his shoulders, with stiff, upright bristles to the middle of his back. His hindquarters appear rather puny compared to his front end. He stands on massive, sturdy legs, with not particularly big tusks.

Size

Boar weight ....136–158 kg (300–350 lb)

Sow weight ....113–129 kg (250–285 lb)

Use

Ancient humans hunted or tracked Wild Boar for meat and fur. Often piglets would be captured during a hunt, and these could be tamed and fattened for meat or breeding. Wild Boar meat has no fat and is low in cholesterol. It fetches a high premium over normal pork.

Related Breeds

From the Wild Boar and its subspecies sprang all the different types of domestic pigs found in Europe and Asia, as a result of interbreeding.

Origin and Distribution

The Sus scrofa species probably originated in South-east Asia (Philippines, Indonesia) and then dispersed across Eurasia. The Wild Boar is still found across northern Europe, the Baltic countries and parts of Russia. It is farmed in Britain.

Philippines, Indonesia

CHAMPION BREEDS

BRED *and* GROOMED to *perfection*, the pigs you are about to see are the *supermodels of the porcine universe.* Unlike their human counterparts, however, there's *no question* of skipping breakfast. These best-in-show beauties are absolutely PROUD TO BE PORKY!

OXFORD SANDY & BLACK
SOW

The Oxford Sandy & Black emerged as a distinct breed around 200 years ago. The Oxford is a large, attractive pig, sandy to ginger in colour, covered with black blotches, and with four white feet and a white tip to its tail. Docile and easily managed, it was the cottage dweller's favourite, and was known as the 'Plum Pudding' pig.

Features

It is medium to large with a long, straight back and fine shoulders. The body should be deep with plenty of heart room and rounded hams. The head is slightly dished with a medium-length nose. The ears are lopped or semi-lopped and not too big. Oxfords are renowned for being good walkers; they have strong legs of medium length with upright pasterns.

Size

Boar weight ....169–179 kg (374–396 lb)

Sow weight ....154–163 kg (340–360 lb)

Use

Oxfords are good mothers and milk well, enabling them to rear 11 piglets easily. They are exceptional foragers and grazers. Weaned at eight weeks, piglets reach pork weight at just 22 weeks of age. Since they lay down a lot less fat than other breeds, they are ideal for bacon. The boars stamp all their offspring with their best genes, making the Oxford a good terminal sire.

Related Breeds

Spotted pigs have been found in Shropshire and other counties in the Midlands of Great Britain for more than 200 years, but the Tamworth and Berkshire breeds have helped to produce the Oxford Sandy & Black.

Origin and Distribution

From its beginnings in Central England, it is now mostly found in the coastal southern counties, and has only been exported to Northern Ireland.

Central England

LARGE BLACK
SOW

The modern LARGE BLACK is derived from two black pig varieties. One was a huge beast from Devon and Cornwall and the other, from south-east England, was very long with shorter legs. Some were dirty white with black, and both were prolific and hardy. Neapolitan and perhaps Chinese blood is also presumed to be present. The herd book was formed around 1900.

Features

Britain's only all-black pig, it has a broad, medium-length head with long, thin lopped ears and a long, clean neck with fine shoulders leading to a very long, strong back and on to wide quarters and broad full hams. It is deep bodied with straight, fine-boned legs and strong pasterns. Its coat must be black, fine and silky. They are docile, extremely good mothers and thrive on unsophisticated pig feed and grass.

Size

Boar weight ....169–179 kg (374–396 lb)

Sow weight ....147–158 kg (325–350 lb)

Use

The Large Black is principally a bacon pig, producing large rashers and hams. It puts on rather more fat than other breeds and therefore has traditionally been crossed with the Large White to produce the once popular, so-called 'blue pig'. The result is very succulent pork and bacon with less fat.

Related Breeds

The Large Black was said to be a cross between the enormous Devon pig and the Sussex and Kent black pigs, with Chinese to reduce the size of the original 17th-century 'Old English Hog'. They were improved during the 20th century.

Origin and Distribution

The Large Black was originally found in the south-west and east of England. Due to its black skin and adaptability it is exported to many hot countries.

South-west
England

MIDDLE WHITE
SOW

The all-white MIDDLE WHITE is a sweet-natured, gentle and docile pig. It is of medium size; a heavier type, though smaller than the Large White, it has fine bones and shorter legs. Its Chinese ancestry shows in its short, dished face and snub nose and tubby appearance. It is economical to keep but needs protection from excessive heat and sunshine and extremes of cold in winter.

Features

The head should be fairly short, dished, with a broad, short nose and width between the eyes. The ears are fairly large and face outwards. The neck's deep girth is in proportion to the great depth of the body, and meets fine, sloping shoulders; the back, long and level with well-sprung ribs and with hams deep and broad. The underline is straight and thick; legs well apart, fairly short and straight with fine bones and upright pasterns. Should give the impression of quality.

Size

Boar weight ....123–139 kg (272–308 lb)

Sow weight ....113–129 kg (250–285 lb)

Use

The Middle White, with its fine bones, has good killing-out percentage, meaning there is less waste when it is butchered. It is a compact pig, early maturing, which produces small porkers in just 16 weeks – too small for most butchers these days, but between the two world wars, thousands were sent to London's meat market.

Related Breeds

It supposedly resulted from a cross between the Large White and the Small White. More likely, it was bred down in size and type by selection. Its herd book was formed in 1884.

Origin and Distribution

Cumberland pigs crossed with Chinese and the Yorkshire were probably the progenitors of the British Middle White. It is now widely found in Japan and Malaysia.

Cumberland, England

BRITISH SADDLEBACK

SOW

In the 17th century, black pigs were favoured in southern England. When Neapolitan and Siamese pigs were used to improve type and succulence, then crossed with the banded New Forest pig, black-and-white pigs were produced. Some had a white belly band that went over the front legs and shoulders. These pigs are hardy, docile and good grazers, and make exceptional mothers. They will thrive on a poor diet.

Features

The colour must be black with a continuous white belt spreading over the shoulders and including the front legs. Its head should be medium in length with a clean-cut jowl and slight dish. Ears are lopped to nearly blinker their sight. Neck clean, no coarseness about the shoulders, back straight and long. Loin broad with medium depth of body and full hams. Legs should be straight and strong with big, straight feet and a fine coat.

Size

Boar weight ....169–179 kg (374–396 lb)

Sow weight ....147–158 kg (325–350 lb)

Use

Used almost exclusively for bacon, this distinctive pig is often crossed with the Large White for blue-and-white bacon pigs. It has a very good food-conversion rate and its piglets grow quickly. It is found in hot countries and is easily kept behind a fence because its ears restrict its vision.

Related Breeds

The old black breeds from south-west England, mixed with those from the south-east and crossed with Neapolitan and Iberian, were mixed with Chinese to refine and improve the large indigenous black pig.

Origin and Distribution

This hardy and extremely adaptable breed has been exported all over the world from its home in England.

England

GLOUCESTERSHIRE OLD SPOT
BOAR

The Gloucestershire Old Spot came to prominence just after the First World War, after the Agriculture Board started the Boar Licensing Scheme in 1913. When a herd book was formed, hundreds were exported all over the world. They became so popular that too much poor-quality stock was used for breeding and the breed faded drastically in number. In 1974 it was classed as endangered.

Features

The Gloucestershire Old Spot is a large white pig with black spots. It has a medium-length head and nose and a dished face with lopped ears. Fine neck with small jowl and fine shoulders. A long level back should end in wide quarters and large hams. It is deep in the body with strong, straight legs. A docile grazer and a hardy outdoor breeder, it was called the 'orchard pig' because it was often kept in orchards.

Size

Boar weight ....169–179 kg (374–396 lb)

Sow weight ....147–158 kg (325–350 lb)

Use

This breed has large hams and is much used as a bacon pig. It is very prolific, having large litters, and is a very good milking mother. It was often crossed with coloured pigs to produce all-white offspring. It was very popular between the two world wars, and many children of that generation may remember it through picture books of the time.

Related Breeds

Similar pigs were found in Staffordshire in the 18th century. Its spots may have come from the 19th-century Oxford Dairy pig, which was light coloured with dark blotches. It is an old breed.

Origin and Distribution

Originally found in the West Country and Midlands of England, it still crops up occasionally in other parts of the world.

England

CHATO MURCIANO

SOW

This delightful, slate-grey pig has a very old Spanish ancestry, hailing from south-eastern Murcia. In 1865 there were 50,000 of them and more than twice as many in 1929. It is thrifty, hardy and easily managed, doing well on farm by-products and waste food; consequently it is suited to many systems of pig keeping, producing succulent lean pork and tasty bacon.

Features

The Chato Murciano was improved by the Large White, Berkshire, Tamworth and the old Celtic pig from Barcelona, called the Victoria. Quite recently the breed was in danger of becoming extinct, but in 1999 the Spanish agricultural authorities set up a programme to prevent this by artificial insemination and cross breeding. The pig has large ears that project outwards and forwards. Its appearance is somewhat coarse, but it has well-fleshed hams.

Size

Boar weight ....123–138 kg (272–308 lb)

Sow weight ....113–129 kg (250–285 lb)

Use

The Chato Murciano produces a good yield of lean meat and excellent bacon. Recently a great deal has been done by the Spanish to promote the excellence of its hams, sobrasada and sausages to the markets of the world. This docile pig has come a long way and will continue to flourish.

Related Breeds

'Chato' means short-nosed. The Chato Victoria and the British Berkshire are in the make-up of the Chato Murciano – both of these had a short nose. The Large White and Tamworth do not have a short nose and were therefore selected to improve this Spanish pig.

Origin and Distribution

This breed comes from the province of Murcia in south-eastern Spain. It is only recently that the Spanish authorities have helped in the development and recovery of this entirely Spanish pig.

Murcia, Spain

TAMWORTH

BOAR

The golden-red TAMWORTH looks stunning when the sun shines on it. They are lively pigs with long legs that can move 'like a racehorse'. Their noses are long, like a plough share, and early in their long history they were known as the 'Forest Pig'. They make good bacon if fed carefully, although they lack a big eye muscle. A superb outdoor pig, but not for the novice.

Features

This breed has a long head, slightly dished with width between the ears and fine jowl. The ears are large and upright. The neck is light and evenly placed on the fine shoulders. The chest is not too deep, and the back is long and deep. The hams are well developed and wide. The legs are shapely and strong with a good quality of bone and short pasterns, so the pig stands up well, with a free action and an alert look.

Size

Boar weight ....169–179 kg (374–396 lb)

Sow weight ....147–158 kg (325–350 lb)

Use

An exceptional pig to 'run out', it will work well as a rotovator or as a clearer of scrub and pernicious weeds. Does not fatten quickly and needs very careful feeding in the latter stages to take to bacon weight because it will run to fat if the feed is not controlled. The bacon produced in this way is delicious.

Related Breeds

The Old Tamworth was red with black, like the Old Berkshire. The Tamworth never had the 19th-century 'improvements' of the Berkshire. Sir Robert Peel brought Irish red pigs to his Tamworth estate. Sir Francis Lawley of Tamworth kept Indian red pigs. In 1750 a red pig came from Barbados to Wiltshire.

Origin and Distribution

The Tamworth was developed in the Midlands in England but is now uncommon in Britain. It has been exported to North America, Australia and New Zealand.

English
Midlands

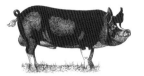

BERKSHIRE

BOAR

The Old Berkshire was a rusty coloured pig with black spots in the late 18th century. Asian blood improved the breed, and Lord Barrington changed it from a large, lop-eared pig to a smaller, prick-eared one. The colour was standardised when the breed society was formed in 1884. Then it was a fashionably fat pig, but now the BERKSHIRE is smart, medium-sized and quick maturing.

Features

The young Berkshire is a naughty pig with a lively character. Its back is long and level and it has a high-set tail with well-sprung ribs. Hams should be wide and deep. The head is fine and wide, with a dished face and medium-length nose. It has fine, sloping shoulders. The legs are straight, strong and wide apart and the Berkshire is well up on its toes, enabling it to walk well. The body is black with some white on the face, feet and tail tip.

Size

Boar weight ....123–138 kg (272–308 lb)

Sow weight ....114–127 kg (252–282 lb)

Use

The Berkshire finishes to pork weight early. It is not suitable for bacon because it becomes too fat if kept longer. Its meat is famous for its quality and taste.

Related Breeds

In the 19th century, black-and-white Berkshires with large lop ears could be found in the British counties of Devon, Norfolk and Gloucestershire; red-and-black Berkshires with prick ears were found in the Midlands. Chinese and Neapolitan pigs were crossed with them.

Origin and Distribution

Originally from Oxfordshire, this breed is now found all over England and Wales and many other countries.

Oxfordshire, England

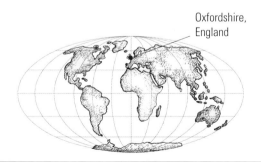

PIÉTRAIN
BOAR

The Piétrain comes from the Belgian village of the same name and was the result of crossing English and French breeds. The extraordinary genetic mutation was noticed in 1920 in the Porabant area, where it was kept. The superbly meaty Piétrain was selected by breeders and taken up by the Belgian pig industry in 1950 because of its double-muscled hams and thick, lean loins.

Features

It is of medium size, white with blue spots and with a medium-sized, neat head. The ears are upright and slightly forward. Its short neck runs into massive shoulders with a large, rounded deep body. The hams are double-muscled and enormous, with a sloping rump. The legs are short and strong. It measures 160 cm (5 ft 3 in) in length and 80 cm (2 ft 8 ins) in height. This solid pig bulges with meat.

Size

Boar weight .... 258–287 kg (570–634 lb)

Sow weight .... 229–258 kg (506–570 lb)

Use

Before the Second World War, pigs were bred to be fat. Later, people wanted lean pork, so the Piétrain came into its own. It has a much higher lean-to-bone ratio than any other pig. It was exported to France and Germany, but never made much of an impression in Britain. It has its problems: if stressed it can drop dead and its extraordinarily large hams and short legs mean it cannot reproduce naturally. It is neither hardy nor vigorous.

Related Breeds

The relatives of the Belgian Piétrain are the French Normand and Bayeux and the British Large White and perhaps the Berkshire or Tamworth. It is derived from the large, muscular pigs of the 19th century. Its herd book was formed in 1958.

Origin and Distribution

The Piétrain is found in Belgium, France and Germany. It has been widely exported as a terminal sire.

Piétrain, Belgium

BRITISH LOP

SOW

These large, long pigs came from the old, white Celtic pigs of Ireland and Wales. They are popular with farmers in the English West Country, the pigs being docile, self-sufficient, hardy, and good grazers and foragers. The BRITISH LOP produces excellent pork and bacon. The breed society was formed in 1918; they keep their own independent herd book.

Features

The pig's head should be of medium length and wide and smooth with long, thin ears that blinker the eyes. Its back is long and level with wide shoulders; it has a wide, strong loin and broad, deep hams. The tail is set on high. The body is deep with well-sprung ribs. Medium-length legs should be straight and level with strong pasterns. The skin is pure white with long, silky hair.

Size

Boar weight ....169–179 kg (374–396 lb)

Sow weight ....147–158 kg (325–350 lb)

Use

It has a long back and is an economical feeder, making it a very good bacon pig. Its rashers have a large eye muscle of meat. It does well outside, grazing and producing plenty of milk for its large litters. It is long-lived and easily managed.

Related Breeds

The British Lop is related to pigs from Northern Ireland, Wales and Cumberland. It is suited to the small farm areas of the West Country and is kept outside all year.

Origin and Distribution

Found mainly in the West Country of England, there is also an enclave in Warwickshire and a large herd in Berwickshire. It repays the farmer with excellent pork and bacon.

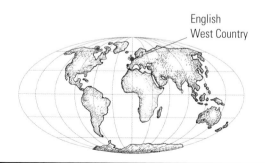

English West Country

LARGE WHITE
S O W

The LARGE WHITE or Yorkshire is probably the most popular pig in the world. They consistently have litters of 10–12 and always milk well. Butchers like them because they produce large meaty porkers and their bacon is legendary for its texture and flavour. In its early history it had big lop ears on a long head. Long in the back with flat sides, it was improved by selective breeding.

Features

The head is fairly long and slightly dished with width between the eyes. It has large prick ears. It has light jowl and clean neck running into full shoulders and a long, slightly arched back. Well-muscled, broad hams to the hocks. A well-set tail with strong, longish, straight legs and plenty of bone, set well apart. Pasterns should be short and strong, as should the feet.

Size

Boar weight ....169–199 kg (374–440 lb)

Sow weight ....159–169 kg (352–374 lb)

Use

The Large White makes a fantastic terminal sire and has been used on indigenous pigs in every European country and a great many others besides. A large pig, it is mainly used for bacon and will consistently produce meaty joints and large rashers. It can be kept with equal ease outdoors or within a commercial indoor system. Both methods produce a valuable carcass.

Related Breeds

Historically there were many farrowed white pigs in the north of England. These Old English lop-eared pigs were the progenitors of the modern Large White.

Origin and Distribution

The Large White came from the north of England, Yorkshire in particular. It is now found all over the world.

Yorkshire, England

DUROC
SOW

The British DUROC was imported from the United States during the 1950s and 1960s by the large commercial pig-breeding companies to use in their breeding programmes. It wasn't until the 1990s, however, that it became accepted in the UK as a pure breed. Its weight gain is phenomenal on a fairly meagre diet. It is a hardy pig, which thrives outdoors during summer and winter.

Features

The most striking thing about the Duroc is its auburn colour. Its head is wide and of medium size with smallish ears bent over like a terrier's. It has a clean jowl and a wide chest; its back is wide, long and slightly arched. The body is deep but standing well off the ground on strong, straight legs and pasterns. It has very well-developed hams and rump with meat to the hocks.

Size

Boar weight ....140–149 kg (310–330 lb)

Sow weight ....131–140 kg (290–310 lb)

Use

The Duroc is classed in England as a 'modern breed'. It makes a superb terminal sire that will improve the meatiness of all the old traditional breeds. It has fat marbling within its meat, producing the most succulent pork in hardy conditions. It is tough and always walks freely.

Related Breeds

The New York Red and the very big Jersey Red hog were cousins of the Duroc in the mid-19th century. Later, other red pigs were imported from England to produce this quick-growing, quiet breed.

Origin and Distribution

Originally from the north-eastern corner of the United States, it is now found in all the pig-keeping states of America and most countries of the world.

North-eastern
USA

HAMPSHIRE

SOW

The HAMPSHIRE probably started its history in the New Forest in England. Black pigs with white saddles were exported to Massachusetts in around 1825; the Americans called them the 'Thin Rind Hog'. The modern HAMPSHIRE has prick ears and, like the Duroc, relatively little body depth. However, it does have muscled, lean shoulders, loin and hams. The boars can be aggressive.

Features

The Hampshire has a medium-sized but wide head. The erect ears are fairly small with a clean jowl and a wide chest. The shoulders are strong and rounded at the top. The back is not over long but is full of muscle. Rump and hams are wide, deep and well muscled. The strong legs are of medium length, never short, with short feet and pasterns. It should walk out in a free way.

Size

Boar weight ....123–138 kg (272–308 lb)

Sow weight ....114–129 kg (252–285 lb)

Use

One of its prime uses is as a terminal sire and it has been widely exported for this reason. Its food conversion rate is superb, producing a high-quality carcass with minimal fat and maximum meat and eye muscle. They are active pigs and good grazers, used almost exclusively on other US breeds for the lean-meat trade. They were imported into Britain in 1968.

Related Breeds

Originally white-belted black pigs from the New Forest in Hampshire, England, they were exported to America and selected by breeding for their lean meat, losing the lop ears and deep body.

Origin and Distribution

From its origins in Hampshire, England, it spread as a terminal sire all over America and was exported to most of the world.

Hampshire, England

WELSH
SOW

The Welsh pig came from very unpromising beginnings. It was described in the 19th century as a razor-backed, coarse-haired, slow-maturing type with very long legs, but the modern pig bears no resemblance to this description. It has become very successful, not unlike the Landrace but with the dish face of the Large White. Its ears are fairly long and lopped. It boasts a very long, strong back and is eminently hardy.

Features

The head should be neat, fine and wide. The ears are lopped with a straight nose and clean jowl and neck. Shoulders fine, flat-topped, running into a strong, long, level back with wide meaty loins. Hams are full and firm, the body not too deep with a thick belly, supported on straight, strong legs with short pasterns and set well apart to walk freely. The skin and coat are fine and white.

Size

Boar weight ....123–138 kg (272–308 lb)

Sow weight ....113–129 kg (250–285 lb)

Use

The Welsh Pig Society was formed in 1920, and this lovely pig became popular from this date – but only, it seems, within Wales. It had all the attributes to rival the Danish Landrace, but never did. It is a superb pork and bacon pig, producing large chops, legs and very meaty, succulent hams and bacon. It is docile and gentle.

Related Breeds

Found in Wales since Viking times, they come from the same type as the Old English Lop, large and Wild Boar-shaped. It has thrived as a result of constructive, selective breeding.

Origin and Distribution

They come from the Cardigan, Carmarthen, Pembroke and Montgomery areas of Wales. They are not widely exported.

Wales

LANDRACE
SOW

The LANDRACE is a Danish export, arriving in Britain in 1949. It is a cross between two original Celtic land pigs of Denmark, with Chinese, Iberian and English breeds, including Middle White and Berkshire and, in the last quarter of the 19th century, the Large White. The Danes were exporting bacon to Britain as far back as 1860; recognising that the Large White would influence their bacon pigs, they imported it.

Features

A medium-length, light head with straight nose and fine jowl and shoulders. Medium-sized flop ears. The back should be long and slightly arched with no dip at the shoulders, leading to the wide loins. Sides not too deep, the quarters broad and straight with full and rounded hams to the hocks. Legs well set on, of medium length, strong with no coarseness and shortish pasterns. They have white hair over pink skin.

Size

Boar weight ....169–199 kg (374–440 lb)

Sow weight ....159–169 kg (352–374 lb)

Use

The productive Landrace is tailor-made for bacon, but also produces excellent pork because it is very lean. It is almost always used as the foundation of commercial hybrid pigs all over Europe and America. Often kept indoors, it does just as well outside, rearing large litters. Landrace sows milk well and are easily managed. The breed society was formed in 1953.

Related Breeds

The indigenous Danish pig of the 15th and 16th centuries was crossed with Chinese and English breeds. With careful breeding the Landrace became a quick-maturing bacon pig.

Origin and Distribution

This long, lean meat pig from Denmark quickly became a commercial success and has influenced breeds in Europe, America and the rest of the world.

Denmark

AMERICAN BERKSHIRE
SOW

The BERKSHIRE arrived in America from England in 1823. The early BERKSHIRE breeders of America and Canada produced a smart meat pig, as opposed to the lard pigs of the time. Soon every pig farmer in North America wanted BERKSHIRES; the breed society was formed way back in 1875. After the Second World War it lost its carcass quality and fell from favour, but it is still respected. New stock was sent from England in 2005.

Features

It is a medium-sized, smart black pork pig with four white feet, a white tail tip and white areas on its face. White is allowed on the body in America, but not in Britain. It has a short dished face and prick ears. Its body is quite long with well-filled hams and fine shoulders on short legs. The sow is docile, milky and hardy. Berkshires produce sweet, lean pork.

Size

Boar weight ....123–138 kg (272–308 lb)

Sow weight ....113–129 kg (250–285 lb)

Use

The American Berkshire, like its English counterpart, is a fine-boned, quick-maturing pork pig. The meat is lean and succulent. It is no good for bacon, as it is too small and, if kept for long, too fat. Its food conversion is high, making it economical to keep, and although it is black-skinned, it kills out completely white.

Related Breeds

The Berkshire was the progenitor of the American, Canadian and German Berkshire, the French Bayeux and also the Bulgarian Dermantsi Pied, with the Spanish Murcia. Originally English, it was described in 1794 as being reddish with black blotches. By 1847 it was black and white.

Origin and Distribution

Exported to the East Coast of the United States from England in 1823, it spread all over the country as a pork pig and terminal sire. It is now found all over the world.

England

CHESTER WHITE

SOW

Nobody really knows the origin of the CHESTER WHITE, though two white pigs, the Cheshire and Yorkshire, from England seem likely candidates. The enormous slab-sided Cheshire, coarse and long-legged, was crossed with the more refined and meatier Yorkshire, then probably mated to the American Suffolk White, which had Chinese blood and was early maturing and fast to finish. The result was a good prolific mother and piglets that grow very large.

Features

This all-white breed from Chester County, Pennsylvania, is a lop-eared, lean-meat pig. The sows are exceptionally milky mothers of large litters. They have broad heads with short noses and dished faces. Full shoulders lead onto a long, straight back and broad loins with full hams. The legs are short and strong, the skin thin with fine hair, making it prone to sunburn.

Size

Boar weight ....169–199 kg (374–440 lb)

Sow weight ....159–169 kg (352–374 lb)

Use

This easily managed, large pig is suitable for both pork and bacon. They can be crossed with Yorkshire, Landrace and also the Duroc to produce plenty of hybrid vigour. Although very prolific, they do not have very good food conversion, but this modern, durable, white pig yields plenty of lean meat.

Related Breeds

This reliable, hardy pig was bred in England during the 19th century from the Cheshire, Old Yorkshire, Bedfordshire and Cumberland. Exported to the United States, it was improved by selective breeding.

Origin and Distribution

Developed in Delaware County and later in Ohio, based on the original whites from Pennsylvania, this pig became widespread in the Midwest, but is rarely seen abroad.

England

AMERICAN YORKSHIRE
SOW

In around 1870, a YORKSHIRE boar was imported to the shore of Lake Ontario from England. It was crossed with the Cheshire, also from England, to produce a square-bodied, large pig with big hams and shoulders. It soon became New York State's most popular pig and was also much favoured in Indiana, Ohio, Iowa and Illinois, where it was prized for its low back fat and lean meat.

Features

The Yorkshire is a large, white pig with small prick ears, a wide dished face and large shoulders. The broad back is arched and the hams are big and rounded. Its legs are light and straight with upright pasterns. The hair is silky and white over pink skin. Sows milk well, are docile and mature early. The boars are prolific and potent, making them excellent terminal sires.

Size

Boar weight ....169–179 kg (374–396 lb)

Sow weight ....147–158 kg (325–350 lb))

Use

The modern Yorkshire is more muscular, with more lean meat. It is predominately used as a bacon pig and has spread all over America. The sows are very fertile and have large litters that average 11 live piglets. The Yorkshire has a good killing-out percentage, because it has fine bones for the size of the pig.

Related Breeds

The Yorkshire has been crossed successfully with the Cheshire, the Chester White, and the Landrace, the offspring of which was often mated with a Duroc boar for a commercial hybrid.

Origin and Distribution

From New York State they spread all over the United States and the rest of the world.

New York State

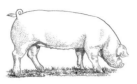

AMERICAN LANDRACE

SOW

The long-bodied, white LANDRACE pig was developed in Denmark and registered in 1906. Between 1927 and 1950 it was greatly improved and became practically the only pig kept in Denmark. It arrived in America in 1934, where it was crossed with indigenous breeds to improve them. Pure-bred or crossed with the white Yorkshire, it produced the bulk of America's bacon. It came to Britain in 1949.

Features

The American Landrace is an all-white, long pig, very prolific and easy breeding; the boars are very potent. The sow has a long nose and large lop ears. The loins and hams are very lean, with practically no fat. The legs are straight and strong with sound feet. It produces a carcass of superb quality from pigs that are excellent mothers and from piglets that grow exceptionally quickly.

Size

Boar weight ....169–179 kg (374–396 lb)

Sow weight ....147–158 kg (325–350 lb)

Use

Often used as a terminal sire. The sows are used to improve other breeds, because their daily live-weight gain and food conversion rate are second to none. They are the mainstay of all European commercial hybrids. The Danish bacon industry was supported by the Landrace, and it headed the bacon industry in Canada, which exported half of all its pig meat to the United States.

Related Breeds

Apart from the American Landrace there are Dutch, Finnish, Swedish, Norwegian, German, Polish, Czech, British and Belgian Landrace, all derived from the original Danish. Some are more compact than the Danish pig.

Origin and Distribution

Originally developed in Denmark, the American Landrace is now found all over the world.

Denmark

AMERICAN DUROC
SOW

The American Duroc is smaller than the Jersey Red with a better carcass and finer frame. One Isaac Frink obtained red pigs from Harry Kelsey of New York State. He owned a famous trotting stallion called Duroc and Frink named his pigs after it. The modern Duroc has an exceptional daily live-weight gain and very good food conversion, making it a particularly good meat pig.

Features

The lovely American Duroc has the most beautiful dark ginger colour. Its medium-sized head is wide with smallish lopped ears. Its neat neck is free of jowl, with large, meaty shoulders and well-sprung chest. The back is well muscled, and slightly arched. The body is cylindrical and supported by strong, straight legs and upright pasterns. The rump and loins are impressively meaty and well developed.

Size

Boar weight ....140–149 kg (310–330 lb)

Sow weight ....131–140 kg (290–310 lb)

Use

The American Duroc is very popular and held in high regard. As a terminal sire it is much favoured to improve the meat carcass of all the older American breeds. It produces exceptionally succulent pork because it has lines of fat within its meat. It is an active breed, healthy and prolific.

Related Breeds

The big Jersey Red and the New York Red were in the Duroc's breeding in the 19th century. In the 20th century, more red pigs were imported from England to produce a fast-maturing, easily managed hog.

Origin and Distribution

This all-American breed was developed in the north-east of America. It has now spread to the rest of the United States and to most parts of the globe.

North-eastern USA

AMERICAN HAMPSHIRE
SOW

The AMERICAN HAMPSHIRE's ancestors came from England in the 19th century and were kept in the southern coastal counties of Dorset, Hampshire and Sussex. Based in the New Forest, the breed was the result of a cross between the black New Forest pig and the Old English sheeted pig. It was later improved with Berkshire, White Suffolk, Chinese and Essex pigs to produce the British Saddleback, with large lop ears. The HAMPSHIRE has developed prick ears.

Features

The modern black-and-white Hampshire has a longish, narrow head, upright ears and no jowl. Large muscled shoulders blend into a barrel body with well-developed loins. The back is slightly arched and the rump slopes down to well-rounded hams. The legs are straight and strong. It walks with a swift, active gait.

Size

Boar weight ....169–179 kg (374–396 lb)

Sow weight ....147–158 kg (325–350 lb)

Use

It has a good food conversion rate and good-sized litters. It is widely used as a terminal sire for the production of pork and bacon, and as an alternative to the Duroc, especially in European countries. It is a good grazer that produces a quality carcass with the minimum of back fat.

Related Breeds

In England there is the British Saddleback, an amalgam of the Wessex Saddleback and the Essex, which in turn produced the American Hampshire.

Origin and Distribution

From Hampshire, England to Massachusetts in the United States, it spread as a terminal sire all over America and was then exported to Europe and most of the rest of the world.

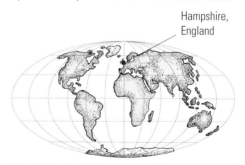

Hampshire, England

SPOTTED SWINE
SOW

This attractive black-and-white pig, large, stocky and tough, is all American. Based on the Poland China, it has strong Berkshire and Gloucestershire Old Spot influences. SPOTTED SWINE are thrifty, self-sufficient outdoor pigs. Sows are best left to look after themselves and their piglets. It is found mainly in Indiana. Its name was fixed as the SPOTTED SWINE or simply Spots in 1960.

Features

It has the overall appearance of being a rugged, coarse-haired, big-boned pig with smallish lop ears on a moderately large head, with a medium-sized snout. The shoulders are powerful and the back long and wide with medium hams. A cylindrical body is supported by strong, thick legs. This pig is active, alert and needs little supervision, making it popular on small farms.

Size

Boar weight ....169–201 kg (374–444 lb)

Sow weight ....159–169 kg (352–374 lb)

Use

Thick and muscular, this breed was never a lard pig. It produces lean meat for either pork or bacon, but rather slowly and not of the highest quality. It can subsist successfully on poor-quality rations and without a lot of care.

Related Breeds

The American Spotted Swine is a mix of Poland China (consisting of the Byfield, Russian, Big China and Irish Grazier) with the Gloucestershire Old Spot and Berkshire. It is not a pig for intensive farming systems.

Origin and Distribution

The American Spotted Swine is a major breed, but not widespread in America. It is found mainly in Indiana and suits the small pig farmers there.

Indiana,
United States

POLAND CHINA

SOW

In 1816 some Big China pigs were taken from Philadelphia to Warren County, Ohio, to improve the indigenous pigs there. The Irish Grazier pig, with its full hams and loins, was bred with Warren County pigs and by 1860 the result was the famous POLAND CHINA, a very large, long-backed coarse pig. The modern POLAND CHINA has become one of the best lean-meat pigs.

Features

This pig's colouring resembles that of a Berkshire – black with white points. Byfield, Big China, Russian and Irish Grazier are in its make-up. It had a herd book in 1878. It used to be the most popular lard pig in America. It is hardy, prolific, self-sufficient and best kept outside.

Size

Boar weight ....169–199 kg (374–440 lb)

Sow weight ....159–169 kg (352–374 lb)

Use

For most of its history the impressive Poland China has been kept as a lard pig, though now it is famed for its meatiness. It is a very good mother and will look after its piglets without interference. The piglets are not as fast-growing as the Durocs or the Hampshires, but some say its pork and bacon cannot be beaten for taste.

Related Breeds

The Poland China is so called because it was bred by a Polish-born farmer from south-west Ohio. The pig had many nicknames but was eventually called Poland China in 1946. Four white breeds were its base, bred to Berkshire.

Origin and Distribution

Originally developed in Warren County, Ohio, it is now widespread across America.

Ohio, United States

EXOTIC BREEDS

CAREFUL cultivation and cross-breeding have produced some *breathtakingly* butch boars and *simply startling* sows. For the TRUE CONNOISSEUR and those with a taste for the unusual, we are proud to present the *finest specimens* from across the globe.

BLONDE MANGALITZA
BOAR

The Blonde Mangalitza is used as a lard pig in its native Hungary. Their meat animals were small primitive types found in Yugoslavia, Romania and Bulgaria as well as in Hungary and Austria. The small Mangalitza originated in Serbia, where southern pigs were crossed with Carpathian breeds to produce a lard pig. It is covered in thick curly hair and, from a distance, looks like a sheep.

Features

The Mangalitza's head is medium length and devoid of wool with lop ears and a longish nose. The body should be deep and long with a large belly. The short legs are straight and strong, free of wool, with black hooves. They are good grazers and do well on poor feed. The body has dense, curly hair, which protects it from heat and cold.

Size

Boar weight ....123–138 kg (272–308 lb)

Sow weight ....113–129 kg (250–285 lb)

Use

The Mangalitza is a lard pig. It is late maturing, developing at around 15 months old. It has very small litters of only three to seven but is exceptionally hardy and disease-free. Their lard is used for cooking and in the making of salami. The fat bacon used to be the staple diet of Hungarian workers.

Related Breeds

Originally the Serbian Sumadija and Siska were developed with Balkan, Romanian, Bulgarian and Moldovan pigs. The breed was fattened for lard with Hungary's enormous maize crop and a large tonnage of maize was exported to Britain between the wars.

Origin and Distribution

The Mangalitza is native to Hungary and is also found in most of Eastern Europe.

Hungary

RED MANGALITZA
BOAR

The RED MANGALITZA was believed to have come about by crossing Romanian, Polish and Yugoslavian pigs with the English Tamworth, but it is more likely to have been crossed with the Bulgarian Kula red pig. The resultant pigs went through many changes, from small prick-eared to the larger lard-type pig of Hungary. This type originally came from Serbia – the reds were favoured by the Austrians, where they are found in small numbers today.

Features

Although the Red Mangalitza has the most uncommon colour, it is the most docile of the Mangalitzas. It has dark-grey skin, with black feet, but is covered in red, woolly, curly hair. This enables the pig to withstand extreme weather conditions. It has good strong legs and does very well on a poor diet. The boars have to have at least 10–12 teats to pass genetically to their offspring; the sows produce small litters.

Boar weight ....123–139 kg (272–308 lb)

Sow weight ....113–129 kg (250–285 lb)

Use

The Red Mangalitza is a late developer but will produce quite a meaty carcass with a good depth of back. Back bacon is eaten all over Eastern Europe, as is Mangalitza salami.

Related Breeds

The mix of the Bulgarian Kula, the Yugoslavian Sumadija and the Romanian Stocli or Baltaret, with perhaps Lincolnshire Curly Coat blood, eventually produced the Red Mangalitza by selective breeding.

Origin and Distribution

This pig was developed in Eastern Europe and favoured in Austria and is still found there; some of these pigs have recently been imported into England.

Hungary

SWALLOW-BELLIED MANGALITZA

SOW

The Swallow-bellied Mangalitza is believed to have been created by crossing the so-called Black or Slate Grey pig with the Black Syrmian in the south of Hungary. This gave us the slate-grey back and body of this woolly pig with its characteristic fair-coloured underbelly. By selective breeding the colour was fixed. The Swallow-belly is smaller and finer than either the Red or the Blonde.

Features

As in all the types and colours of woolly Mangalitzas, the Swallow-Belly is a contented pig and adapts to most pig-raising regimes without complaint. It has the lopped ears, but finer bones than the Red or the Blonde, and is supported on slender legs and smaller feet. It used to be an enormous lard pig but is now bred considerably smaller.

Size

Boar weight ....113–129 kg (250–285 lb)

Sow weight ....102–111 kg (225–245 lb)

Use

Still kept pure by small farmers in Hungary and surrounding countries, this pig is now mostly crossed with a commercial white pig to produce a meatier carcass with less fat.

Related Breeds

In Hungary, the Bakony was a relation of the Mangalitza, as was the Croatian Siska and the Serbian Sumadija. It is believed that it was the Bakony pig that gave the Mangalitza its woolly coat.

Origin and Distribution

Found in Eastern Europe, more especially in Hungary in the mountains as well in as the Great Hungarian plain, it was first exported to England in the 1990s.

Hungary

BLACK VIETNAMESE POT-BELLIED
SOW

The BLACK VIETNAMESE POT-BELLIED pig was developed as a dwarf pig from a Vietnamese breed in the 1960s. Originally imported into Sweden and Canada as a zoo exhibit, their use as pets began when they were taken to the United States. Suddenly an unbelievable craze to own a pet pig started among affluent Americans; they sold for thousands of dollars, even though their temperament was suspect when they grew older, especially in the males.

Features

The original Pot-bellied pig was very fat and larger. They were black, with very wrinkled faces and sway backs, and very short, thick legs with flattened pasterns. Now they are smaller, less fat and have almost lost the dip in their backs. The legs are finer and straighter. There are other colours now and they are hairier – they have been bred to be more attractive.

Size

Boar weight .... 45–54 kg (100–120 lb)

Sow weight .... 31–45 kg (70–100 lb)

Use

If this little pig is slaughtered young enough, before it gets too fat, it can be used as a meat pig. As pets, they are nowhere near as popular as they used to be. They stand about 42 cm (16 in) tall, and with a short nose they are supposed to look cute. They only breed once a year and have quite large litters of tiny piglets.

Related Breeds

The Vietnamese Pot-bellied pig comes from South-east Asia. It is thought to have Chinese ancestry because it is typical of the pigs that come from that part of the world.

Origin and Distribution

Originally from Vietnam, they have been taken all over the world because of the American craze for them.

Vietnam

WHITE VIETNAMESE POT-BELLIED

BOAR

The WHITE VIETNAMESE POT-BELLIED pig is believed to have come from the north-east border of China because it looks very similar to the Mong Cai. It is believed that all pot-bellied pigs are descended from the ancient wild pig Artiodactyl suina. The Mong Cai was originally a black-and-white pig: some of these were exported to Sweden and England, and from there to Indiana, USA, where pure white ones were bred.

Features

The White Vietnamese Pot-Bellied pig is slightly larger than the Black. It has more hair and is heavier boned than its cousin. The Black has very fine bones and is more sway-back than the White, which has dark-grey skin patches on its body but with the familiar black hooves of the Black. Being less sway-backed, their bellies do not sweep the ground, and they have very short, thick legs.

Size

Boar weight .... 49–56 kg (110–125 lb)

Sow weight .... 36–45 kg (80–100 lb)

Use

These little pigs make very good pets because they have been bred to have better temperaments than the Black Vietnamese Pot-Bellied variety. They are programmed to farrow only once a year and produce large litters of very small piglets.

Related Breeds

The Co from Central Vietnam is a relation, and so is the Heo Moi from South Vietnam. These two cousins are smaller than the White Vietnamese Pot-Bellied pig, and weigh less than 50 kg (110 lb).

Origin and Distribution

They came from the north-east border of China, then spread to Sweden and England and then to Indiana in the United States.

North-east China

KUNE KUNE

SOW

T HE KUNE KUNE, which means 'fat and round', is a Maori pig from New Zealand with an uncertain history. Nobody knows quite how this little pig got there. The Maori say they brought them, with their pet rats for eating, from the Polynesian Islands in their canoes. This is possible, if they restrained them by their legs on the voyage. Others say the whaling ships brought them to provide fresh meat.

Features

The knee-high Kune Kune is round and tubby with a turned-up nose and dished face, with two wattles under its chin, and comes in various colours. The smallish ears can be pricked or lopped and the boar has heavy jowls and shoulders. The body is deep, medium length, with rounded hams and very short legs. It is very hairy and never curls its tail. They have small litters and mature late, but fatten on grass alone.

Size

Boar weight .... 49–59 kg (110–132 lb)

Sow weight .... 39–49 kg (88–110 lb)

Use

The Maori kept their pigs for lard, in which they preserved their dried meat. They did not usually eat them except when celebrating a particular event. Elsewhere the surplus boars are turned into sausages, while the hams make succulent and tasty pork joints. The others are sold as outdoor pets.

Related Breeds

The Kune Kune might have come from China. They certainly show Chinese characteristics with their short noses, short legs and tubby bodies. It is possible they came from South-east Asia. New Guinea also has a little pig that resembles the Kune Kune.

Origin and Distribution

In 1992 the first Kune Kunes were exported from New Zealand into Britain. They are now found in Ireland, France, the Netherlands and the United States.

New Zealand

REPORTAGE

A CANDID and revealing glimpse behind the scenes at the tension, *anticipation* and excitement that builds as our would-be PORCINE CHAMPIONS and their *proud owners* primp, preen and prepare to step out onto the hallowed straw of the *world's most celebrated pig shows.*

The Hatfield House Country Show, UK

The annual Hatfield House Country Show is a chance for champion pigs to strut their stuff.

Showing off your best side.

The future's looking rosy.

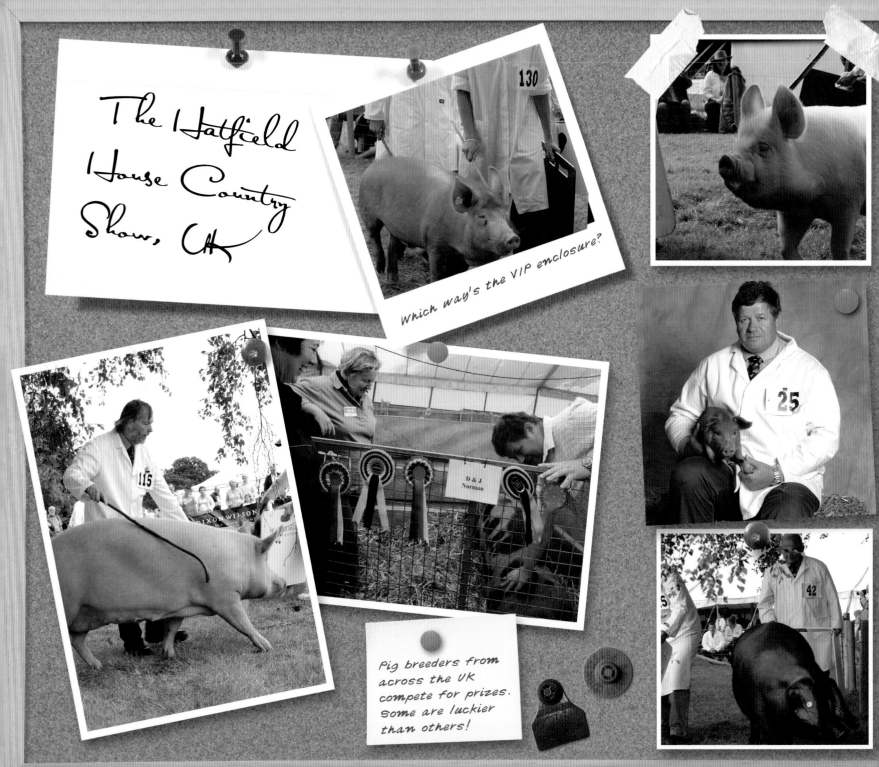

The Hatfield House Country Show, UK

Which way's the VIP enclosure?

Pig breeders from across the UK compete for prizes. Some are luckier than others!

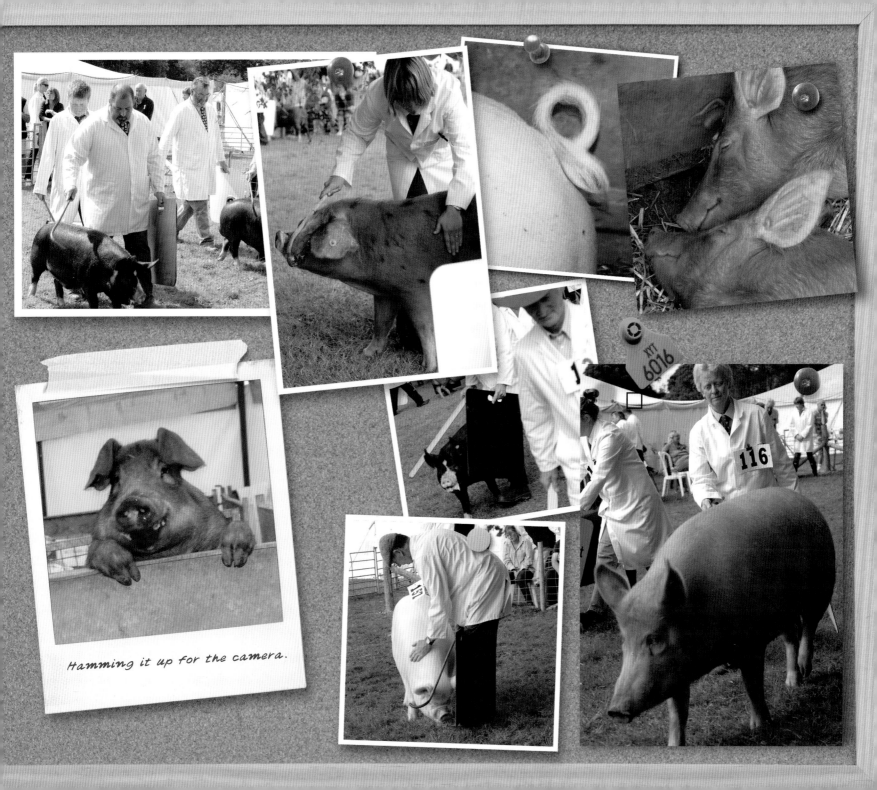

Hamming it up for the camera.

Keystone International Livestock Exposition, USA

Hey, isn't that Kevin Bacon over there?

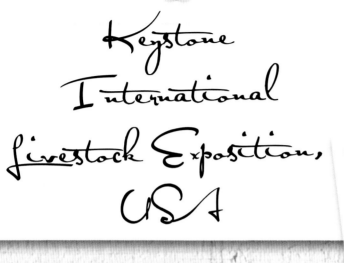

Chilling out with friends backstage.

Hundreds of pigs are exhibited each year at the Keystone International Livestock Exposition in Pennsylvania, USA.

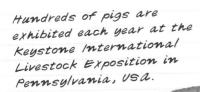

K·P HOGS

AMANDA ~ FAYE PENNINGTON
ED KREVEL
2760 SYLVIS ROAD, CURRY TREE, PA
814-743-5228

Keystone International Livestock Exposition, USA

RESERVE CHAMPION

KEYSTONE INTERNATIONAL LIVESTOCK EXPOSITION

HARRISBURG PENNSYLVANIA

I'll put this shot on Facebook.

The Keystone Expo is the largest livestock show in the eastern United States.

I'm a celebrity - get me out of here!

SEPOR
Pig Show,
Spain

a star is born.

Spain is famous
for its Serrano ham,
and boasts nearly
2,000 producers of
the product.

Call my agent – I can't work
under these conditions!

It is estimated
that the average
annual consumption
of cured ham in
Spain is 5 kg (11 lb)
per person.

SEPOR
Pig Show,
Spain

There are more than 20 million pigs in Spanish farms. No wonder competition is so fierce.

Two good reasons why I should win.

These little piggies
went to market...

Mangalitzas, Austria

The Mangalitza pig is an ancient curly-coated breed from Austria and Hungary. The Austrian Mangalitza Pig Breeders Association was formed to promote this rare pig and increase its population. Seventeen Mangalitzas were imported into Britain in 2006.

Mangalitza sows make very good mothers and the piglets enjoy human company, making them popular with smallholders.

In Germany the Mangalitza is known as the Wollschwein, or 'woolly pig' – for obvious reasons. Its coat is thick and curly in winter but it moults in warmer weather.

Do they have a 'cute' category at these pig shows?

GLOSSARY

Arc Pig house made of semi-circular metal sheets

Action The way a pig walks

Bat A flat stick measuring about 1.2 m (4 ft) long by 2½ in (6.4 cm) wide, which is made of board and used to control a pig

Boar Male pig

Commercial pigs Pigs kept in large numbers, for profit

Conformation Configuration of the pig and body proportions

Eye muscle Round, lean meat of a loin chop

Farrowing Giving birth

Fattening pig A pig being fattened for pork or bacon

Food conversion The amount of food the pig consumes to produce a pound or kilogram of meat

Gilt Young female that has not had piglets

Hams The large muscles/meat on the backside of a pig

Herd book Official record and history of a pure breed; contains birth registrations for pedigrees

Hybrid Offspring from cross-breeding. For example, the first-generation offspring, F1 hybrid, will have more favourable genes than their parents, and will be dominant over the less favourable

Jowl The heavy folds under the throat

Killing-out percentage The difference between the live weight and carcass weight

Live-weight gain The amount of weight put on in so many days or weeks

Lopped Ears that fall over the face and blinker the pig's sight

Modern Certain breeds are classed as such: Large White, Landrace, Welsh, Duroc, Hampshire and Chester White

Pastern The part of the leg between the hoof and the fetlock

Pedigree The certificate of registration showing the pure-bred generations of a pig

Pig board A 61-cm (2-ft) square board with a handhold cut out at the top, used to guide a pig

Points The extremities: feet, nose and tip of tail

Porker Young pig of around 6 months old, weighing 63.5 kg (140 lb) fit to be turned into pork

Potency Virility

Rare breed A pig breed classed as at risk

Registered Certified by a pig authority to have a pedigree

Run out A pig that is run out is kept outside and allowed to forage over an area

Semi lopped Ears that are inclined forward

Sheeted A coloured pig that has a very large band of white around the body between contrasting colours at the front end and the back end

Slab sided A narrow pig with a prominent back bone

Sow Female pig

Terminal sire A boar used on a crossbred sow

Thrifty A pig that is economical to feed; it doesn't require a lot of food to put on meat

Traditional Non-commercial pigs, usually coloured but not always, such as Berkshire, British Lop, Large Black, Oxford Sandy & Black, Saddleback, and Tamworth

Underline The udders of a pig or the double row of teats

Wattles The fleshy protuberances that hang down under a pig's jaw on either side

Weaners Piglets weaned off their mothers

SHOWS & ASSOCIATIONS

The following is a list of major agricultural/livestock shows and associations:

SHOWS

Europe

THE HATFIELD HOUSE COUNTRY SHOW
Hatfield House
Hatfield, Hertfordshire
AL9 5NQ
UK
Website www.hatfield-house.co.uk/countryshow
Telephone +44 (0) 1707 287010

THE ROYAL HIGHLAND SHOW
Royal Highland Centre
Ingliston, Edinburgh
EH28 8NF
UK
Website www.royalhighlandshow.org
Telephone +44 (0) 131 335 6200
Email showdept@rhass.org.uk

THE ROYAL SHOW
The Royal Agricultural Society of England
Stoneleigh Park, Warwickshire
CV8 2LZ
UK
Website www.royalshow.org.uk
Telephone +44 (0) 2476 696 969
Email membership@rase.org.uk

THE ROYAL WELSH SHOW
The Royal Welsh Agricultural Society
Llanelwedd, Builth Wells
Powys
LD2 3SY
UK
Website www.rwas.co.uk/en/welsh-show/
Telephone +44 (0) 1982 553683
Email requests@rwas.co.uk

SEPOR
Recinto Ferial de Lorca
Apartado de Correos 139
30800 Lorca (Murcia)
Spain
Website www.seporlorca.com/ing/index.asp
Telephone +34 968 468 978
Email sepor@lorca.es

USA

KEYSTONE INTERNATIONAL LIVESTOCK EXHIBITION
Pennsylvania Farm Show Complex & Expo Center
2300 North Cameron Street
Harrisburg
PA 17110-9443
USA
Website www.agriculture.state.pa.us/kile/site/default.asp
Telephone +1 (717) 787 2905

THE NORTH AMERICAN LIVESTOCK EXHIBITION
937 Phillips Lane
Louisville
KY 40233-7130
USA
Website www.livestockexpo.org/
Telephone +1 (502) 595 3166
Email kfecnaile@ksfb.ky.gov

New Zealand

ROYAL NEW ZEALAND SHOW
Canterbury A&P Association
PO Box 9002, Tower Junction
Christchurch 8149
New Zealand
Website www.theshow.co.nz
Telephone +64 3 343 3033
Fax +64 3 343 3110

ASSOCIATIONS

Europe

ASOCIACION INTERPROFESIONAL DEL CERDO IBERICO (ASICI)
Apdo. de Correos 247 06300 Zafra
Badajoz
Spain
Website www.iberico.com/
Telephone +34 924 554610
Email iberico@iberico.com

ASSOCIATIONS continued

AUSTRIAN MANGALITZA ASSOCIATION
Wischathal 20
2013 Göllersdorf, NO
Austria
Website www.mangalitza.at
Email igwoe.zuchtbuch@utanet.at

BERKSHIRE PIG BREEDERS CLUB
Berkshire Pig Breeders Club
Website www.berkshirepigs.org.uk
Email enquiries@berkshirepigs.org.uk

BRITISH KUNE KUNE PIG SOCIETY
Website www.britishkunekunesociety.org.uk/
Telephone +44 (0) 1799 525421

BRITISH LOP PIG SOCIETY
Website www.britishloppig.org.uk/
Telephone +44 (0) 1948 880243
Email secretary@britishloppig.org.uk

BRITISH PIG ASSOCIATION
Trumpington Mews
40b High Street
Trumpington, Cambridge
CB2 9LS
UK
Website www.britishpigs.org
Telephone +44 (0) 1223 845096
Email bpa@britishpigs.org

BRITISH SADDLEBACK BREEDERS CLUB
Dryft Cottage
South Cerney
Cirencester, Gloucestershire
GL7 5UB
UK
Website www.saddlebacks.org.uk/
Email mail@saddlebacks.org.uk

GLOUCESTERSHIRE OLD SPOTS PIG BREEDERS CLUB
Website www.oldspots.org.uk/
Email mail@oldspots.org.uk

LARGE BLACK BREEDERS CLUB
Website www.largeblackpigs.co.uk/
Email kenworthyflock@fsmail.net

MIDDLE WHITE BREEDERS CLUB
Telephone 01285 860229
Email miranda@middlewhites.freeserve.co.uk

OXFORD SANDY & BLACK PIG SOCIETY
Website www.oxfordsandypigs.co.uk/
Telephone +44 (0) 1722 718263
Email osbpigs@homecall.co.uk

THE PEDIGREE WELSH PIG SOCIETY
Telephone +44 (0) 7966 583896
Email lorni-lou@fsmail.net

TAMWORTH BREEDERS CLUB
Website www.tamworthbreedersclub.co.uk/
Telephone +44 (0) 1522 778757
Email secretary@tamworthbreedersclub.co.uk

USA

AMERICAN BERKSHIRE ASSOCIATION
Website www.americanberkshire.com/
Telephone +1 (765) 497 3618
Email berkshire@nationalswine.com

NATIONAL SWINE REGISTRY (USA)
Website www.nationalswine.com/
Telephone +1 (765) 463-3594
Email nsr@nationalswine.com

NORTH AMERICAN POT-BELLIED PIG ASSOCIATION
Website www.petpigs.com/
Telephone +1 (480) 266 8755

New Zealand

THE NEW ZEALAND KUNE KUNE ASSOCIATION
PO Box 9085
Hamilton
New Zealand
Website www.kunekune.co.nz
Telephone +64 7 823 6044

Picture credits
Corbis/Historical Picture Archive:
20 TL, 20 TR, 20 BR, 25, 27, 29.
Getty Images/Dorling Kindersley: 31.
iStockphoto: 10; © Tim Burrett: 13.
Mary Evans Picture Library: 20 BL, 23.

Cover photograph **Gloucestershire Old Spot**
by Paul Farnham

AUTHOR'S ACKNOWLEDGEMENTS

To my wife and help-mate Maureen who, with me, built our pig herd up to what it is today; who really started it all by pestering me to buy her a couple of Berkshire gilts, all those years ago. I owe her so much.

I would also like to thank my dear friend Laura Henderson, who typed, edited and printed my words in such a short time, so efficiently, so willingly and so cheerfully, I extend my warmest thanks.

My thanks must also go to Tom Kitch and Lorraine Turner of Ivy Press: Tom for giving me the opportunity to write the words for the lovely pictures of these beautiful pigs, and Lorraine for guiding my footsteps along the way.

PUBLISHER'S ACKNOWLEDGEMENTS

The publisher would like to thank all the pig associations and organisations for their assistance with this book. We would also like to express our gratitude to the pig owners and breeders for their help and co-operation in arranging the photo shoots at the agricultural shows, farms and country estates:

American Berkshire Calvin Lazarus family
American Duroc Calvin Lazarus family
American Hampshire Calvin Lazarus family
American Landrace Calvin Lazarus family
Berkshire Charles Bull
Black Vietnamese Pot-bellied Paul Leven
Blonde Mangalitza Christoph Wiesner
British Lop Mark Edgar
British Saddleback J.R. & M.L. Wreakes
Chester White Calvin Lazarus family
Chato Murciano José Reverte Navarro
Duroc Hayley Loveless
Gloucestershire Old Spot Stephen Booth
Hampshire M.J. Kiddy and son
Kune Kune Andy Case
Landrace Jaime Torrento Calmet
Large Black A. W. Acreman
Large White Steve Loveless
Middle White Brian Merry
Oxford Sandy & Black Maureen and Andy Case
Piétrain Antonio Pollan Martinez
Poland China Calvin Lazarus family
Red Mangalitza Christoph Wiesner
Spotted Swine Calvin Lazarus family
Swallow-bellied Mangalitza Christoph Wiesner
Tamworth Viscount Cranborne
Welsh Christine Vaughan
White Vietnamese Pot-bellied Paul Leven
Yorkshire Calvin Lazarus family

INDEX

A
agricultural shows
  directory of 110
  early years 14
  Hatfield House, UK 96–9, 110
  judging at 17
  Keystone, USA 100–3, 110
  Mangalitza, Austria 108–9
  preparing for 16
  SEPOR, Spain 104–7, 110
  summer shows 15
American Berkshire 64, **65**
American Duroc 72, **73**
American Hampshire 74, **75**
American Landrace 70, **71**
American Yorkshire 68, **69**
associations 110–11

B
Berkshire 11, 12, 13, 48, **49**
  American Berkshire 64, **65**
  Berkshire 48, **49**
  Old Berkshire 24, **25**
Blonde Mangalitza 82, **83**
breeds 12
  around the world 13
  development of 11
British Lop 12, 52, **53**
British Saddleback 12, 13,
  13, 40, **41**
buying pigs 18

C
caring for pigs 18–19
Chato Murciano 44, **45**
Chester White 66, **67**
Chinese pigs 11
Christmas fairs 14
Cumberland 12

D
domestication, history of 10
Duroc 12, 13, 56, **57**
  American Duroc 72, **73**
  Duroc 56, **57**

E
East Anglian 11

F
fodder beet 19

G
glossary 110
Gloucestershire Old Spot 12,
  42, **43**
grooming 16

H
Hampshire 12, **16**, 58, **59**
  American Hampshire 74, **75**
  Hampshire 58, **59**
Hatfield House show, UK 96–9, 110
housing 18

K
keeping pigs 18–19
Keystone show, USA 100–3, 110
Kune Kune 15, 92, **93**

L
Landrace 12, 13, 62, **63**
  American Landrace 70, **71**
  Landrace 62, **63**
Large Black 12, 13, 36, **37**
Large White (previously Yorkshire)
  12, 13, 54, **55**
Lincolnshire Curly Coat 12
livestock markets 14

M
Mangalitza pigs
  Blonde Mangalitza 82, **83**
  Red Mangalitza 84, **85**
  Swallow-bellied Mangalitza
  86, **87**
Mangalitza show, Austria 108–9
Middle White 12, 38, **39**
moving pigs 19

N
Neapolitan 11, 22, **23**
Neolithic period 10

O
Old Berkshire 24, **25**
Old English 26, **27**
Oxford Sandy & Black **11**, 12,
  34, **35**

P
paddocks 19
Piétrain 50, **51**
piglets 9
  weaning of 19
Poland China 78, **79**

R
Red Duroc 56, **57**
Red Mangalitza 84, **85**
Romans, the 10

S
SEPOR pig show, Spain 104–7, 110
shows *see* agricultural shows
Siamese 11, 28, **29**
sows, maternal instincts of 9
Spotted Swine 76, **77**
Swallow-bellied Mangalitza 86, **87**

T
Tamworth 12, **12**, 13, 16, 46, **47**

V
Vietnamese Pot-bellied pigs
  Black Vietnamese Pot-bellied 88, **89**
  White Vietnamese Pot-bellied 90, **91**

W
weaners, buying 18
weaning piglets 19
Welsh 12, 60, **61**
White Yorkshire 11
Wild Boar 10, **10**, 30, **31**

Y
Yorkshire
  American Yorkshire 68, **69**
  White Yorkshire 11
  see also Large White
Young Farmers' Clubs 15